Usborne Activities

Little Sticker Dolly Dressing

Christmas fairy

Use the stickers to dress the fairies and decorate the pages in this magical sticker book.

usborne.com

Usborne Publishing Ltd.,
83-85 Saffron Hill, London,
EC1N 8RT, England.

Usborne Verlag, Usborne Publishing Ltd.,
Prüfeninger Str. 20, 93049 Regensburg,
Deutschland, VK Nr. 17560

CE UK CA

£5.99
CAD$10.95

JFMAM JASOND/22
7458/1

FSC
www.fsc.org

ISBN 978-1-474-99922-9

9 781474 999229

W9-CRO-665

Printed in China

Little Sticker Dolly Dressing Christmas fairy

Written by Fiona Watt

Illustrated by Lizzie Mackay

Designed by Johanna Fürst

Contents

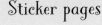

Merrie the Christmas fairy

Merrie the fairy dreams that this Christmas will be
a very magical time for everyone in Fairyland.
She's asked her fairy friends to make her wishes come true.

Dress Merrie in her fairy clothes, then decorate
the pages with the rest of the stickers.

Merrie

Merrie hopes to decorate a Christmas tree
to surprise all the forest fairies.

Dewdrop

4

Pippin

Glistening icicles

Dewdrop and Pippin are gathering sparkly icicles
to hang on Merrie's tree. They gently snap tiny icicles
from branches and lay them in little baskets.

Linden

Posy

6

Making garlands

Linden, Posy and Merrie have gathered
nuts, berries and leaves from the forest floor.
They're threading them delicately onto strings,
to make long Christmas tree garlands.

Merrie

Neve

Sparkling snowflakes

As snowflakes tumble, Neve and Crystal flutter
high into the icy sky, to catch snowflakes
to scatter around the tree.

Crystal

9

Nixie

Pine forest

Nixie and Cassia are searching for
sweet-smelling pinecones. They tiptoe through
a secret fairy forest, where lots of pine trees grow.

Cassia

11

Flashing fireflies

Florian, Merrie and Lucia flutter into the
night sky to collect glowing fireflies. They gather
them in jars, to light the magical tree.

Florian

Merrie

Lucia

13

Merrie

Rowan

Holly berries

Birds twitter and tweet in holly bushes,
as Rowan helps Merrie pick the shiny red
berries to add to the branches of her tree.

Merrie

Starry sky

The fairies' wings twinkle in the moonlight, as
Merrie and Luno soar into the night sky in search of
a special star to place on the top of Merrie's tree.

Luno

Decorating the tree

The air is filled with fluttering wings, as little
fairies add the garlands of nuts and berries,
glowing fireflies, pinecones, sparkling icicles
and snowflakes to Merrie's Christmas tree.

Fairy godmother

The tree is now decorated, but Merrie's unsure about her special surprise for everyone in Fairyland. She's come to visit her fairy godmother to ask her for help.

Merrie

Fairy godmother

Magical fairy dust

As Merrie waves her hand, fairy dust given to her
by her godmother, floats through the air. Lots and
lots of extra sparkle, lights up the tree.

Merrie

Merrie

The night before Christmas

As the moon shines through Merrie's bedroom
window, she hopes everyone in Fairyland will
enjoy her magical Christmas tree.

First published in 2022 by Usborne Publishing Ltd, 83-85 Saffron Hill, London, EC1N 8RT England. usborne.com Copyright © 2022
Usborne Publishing Ltd. The name Usborne and the balloon logo are trade marks of Usborne Publishing Ltd. All rights reserved. No part
of this publication may be reproduced, stored in a retrieval system, or transmitted in any form or by any means without prior permission
of Usborne Publishing Ltd. UE First published in America 2022, EDC, Tulsa, Oklahoma 74146 usbornebooksandmore.com

Merrie the Christmas fairy

Pages 2 -3

Merrie's headdress

Put Merrie's skirt on before her jacket

A lantern for Merrie to hold

Glistening icicles

Pages 4 –5

Dewdrop's headdress and outfit

Pippin's hat and clothes

Linden's hat
and clothes

Merrie's clothes

Posy's outfit

Merrie's
boots

Sparkling snowflakes
Pages 8 - 9

Neve's net for catching snowflakes

Put Neve's cloak on after her skirt

Crystal's outfit

Nixie's headdress

Nixie's outfit

Cassia's clothes

Flashing fireflies
Pages 12 –13

Florian's headdress

Florian's jacket

Put Lucia's skirt on before her cloak.

Merrie's outfit

Holly berries
Pages 14 – 15

Put Merrie's skirt on before her jacket.

Rowan's outfit

Starry sky
Pages 16 –17

Put Merrie's skirt on first

Decorating the tree
Pages 18 - 19

Fairy godmother
Pages 20 - 21

Merrie's headdress and outfit

The fairy godmother's top and skirt

Magical fairy dust
Pages 22 - 23

Merrie's headdress
and clothes

The night before
Christmas
Page 24

Put Merrie's
bottoms on before
her top.